The Great Sing Along Party Book

D1602161

Table of Contents

Aba Daba Honeymoon

Words and Music by
Arthur Fields and Walter Donovan

Moderately

"Ab - a, dab - a, dab - a, dab - a, dab - a, dab - a, dab," Said the Chim - pie to the Monk, "Bab - a, dab - a, dab - a, dab - a, dab - a, dab - a, dab," Said the Mon - key to the Chimp. All night long they'd chat - ter a - way,— All day long they're hap - py and gay,— Swing - ing and sing - ing in their hun - ky, ton - key way.

After You've Gone

Words and Music by
Henry Creamer and Turner Layton

Alice Blue Gown

Words by Joseph McCarthy
Music by Harry Tierney

In my sweet lit - tle A - lice Blue Gown, ____ When I first wan - dered down in to town, ____ I was both proud and shy, As I felt ev' - ry eye, But in ev' - ry shop win - dow I'd primp, pass - ing by; Then in man - ner of fash - ion I'd frown, ____ And the world seem'd to smile all a - round, ____ Till it wilt - ed I wore it, I'll al - ways a - dore it, My sweet lit - tle A - lice Blue Gown.

Anytime

Words and Music by Herbert Happy Lawson

Moderately

prove your love for me is true._____ An - y

Time _____ you're think - ing 'bout me, _____ That's the

time _____ I'll be think - ing of you, _____ So An - y

time you say you want me back a - gain, That's the time I'll

come back home to you. An - y you._____

April Showers

Words by B.G. DeSylva
Music by Louis Silvers

With an easy flow

Life is not a high-way strewn with flow-ers,_____ still it holds a good-ly share of bliss._____ When the sun gives way to A-pril show-ers_____ here's the point that you should nev-er miss._____ Though A-pril

see clouds up - on the hills, you soon will

see crowds of daf - fo - dils; so keep on

look - ing for a blue - bird and lis - t'ning for his song, when - ev - er A - pril

show - ers come a - long. Though A - pril - long.

By The Beautiful Sea

Words by Harold R. Atteridge
Music by Harry Carroll

Brightly

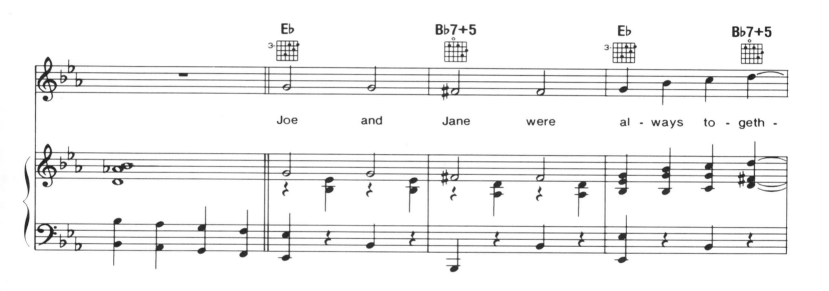

Joe and Jane were al-ways to-geth-

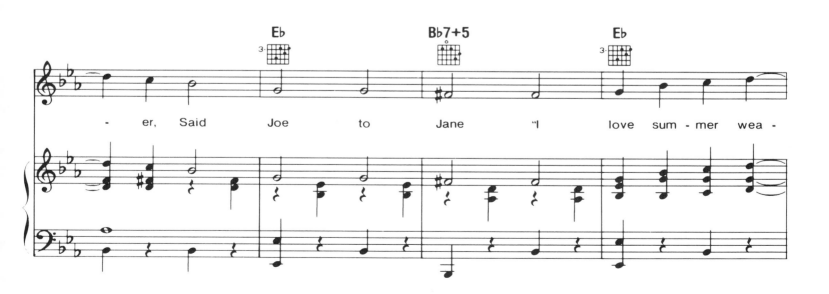

-er, Said Joe to Jane "I love sum-mer wea-

for her   So he'd get ___ his Ford   Hol - ler "All ___

___ a - board   Gee!   I   want   to   be:" _____

___   By   the   sea,   by   the   sea   By   the

beau - ti - ful   sea ___   You   and   I,   you   and

The Caissons Go Rolling Along

Words and Music by Edmund L. Gruber

With movement

1. O - ver hill, o - ver dale, We have hit the dust - y
2. To the front, day and night, Where the dough - boys dig and

trail,) And those cais - sons go roll - ing a - long.
fight,)

"Count - er march! right - a - bout!" Hear those wag - on sol - diers
Our bar - rage will be there, Fired ____ on the rock - ets

shout,) While those cais - sons go roll - ing a - long.
flare,)

Chicago

Words and Music by Fred Fisher

Medium Bounce

Chorus

CHI - CA - GO,— CHI - CA - GO,— That tod-dl - in' town— (tod- dl - in' town—) CHI - CA - GO,— CHI - CA - GO, I'll show you a - round, I love it!

Bet your bot-tom dol - lar you lose the blues— in CHI - CA - GO,— CHI - CA - GO,— The folks who vis - it all wan-na set - tle down.—

22

On State Street, That great street,— I just wan-na say,—
(just wan-na say,) They do things— they don't do on Broad-way,
say, You'll have the time, the time— of your life, Bring all your friends, your kids—
— and your wife, to CHI - CA - GO,— CHI - CA-GO my home town.—

CHI -

Danny Boy

Words by Frederick Edward Weatherly

back   when sum-mer's in the   mea - dow, ____   or when the   val -   ley's hush'd and white with
hear,   tho' soft your tread a - bove__ me, ____   and all my dreams   will warm and swee - ter

snow. _____   'Tis I'll be   there   in sun-shine or in   shad - ow, ____   oh, Dan - ny
be. _____   If you will not fail   to tell me that you   love__ me, ____   then I shall

Boy, oh Dan - ny Boy, I   love you   so! _____
sleep in peace un - til you come to   me! _____

no chord

But   if   ye

Darktown Strutters' Ball

Words and Music by Shelton Brooks

Moderately

I'll be down to get you in a tax-i, Hon-ey, You bet-ter be read-y a-bout half past eight,__ Now dear-ie, don't be late,__ I want to be there when the band starts play-ing. Re-mem-ber when we get there, Hon-ey, The two-steps, I'm goin' to have 'em all,__ Goin' to dance out both my shoes,__ When they play the "Jel - ly Roll Blues", To-mor-row night at The Dark-town Strut-ters' Ball.

How 'Ya Gonna Keep 'Em Down On The Farm
(After They've Seen Pareé)

Words by Sam M. Lewis and Joe Young
Music by Walter Donaldson

How 'ya gon - na keep 'em, down on the farm, ___ Af - ter they've seen ___ Pa - ree? ___ How 'ya gon - na keep 'em a -

27

29

For Me And My Gal

Words by Edgar Leslie and E. Ray Goetz
Music by George W. Meyer

I Never Knew
(I Could Love Anybody Like I'm Loving You)

**Words and Music by Tom Pitts,
Ray Egan, Roy K. Marsh**

35

If You Were The Only Girl
In The World

Words by Clifford Grey
Music by Nat D. Ayer

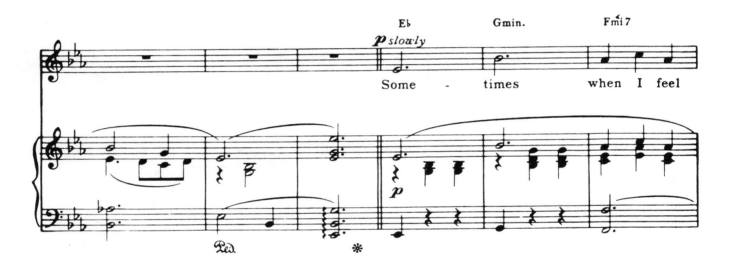

Some - times when I feel

bad and things look blue,_____ I

REFRAIN (*very slow and with much expression*)

*Male or female version as desired

I'll Be With You In Apple Blossom Time

Words by Neville Fleeson
Music by Albert Von Tilzer

If I Had My Way

Words by Lou Klein
Music by James Kendis

42

I'm Forever Blowing Bubbles

Words and Music by
Jaan Kenbrovin and John William Kellette

Ja·Da

Words and Music by Bob Carleton

K·K·K·Katy

By Geoffrey O'Hara

A Little Bit Of Heaven
(Shure They Called It Ireland)

Words by J. Keirn Brennan
Music by Ernest R. Ball

here's the way me dear old moth-er told the tale to me:___
lit - tle bit of Heav - en, and I love it more and more.___

Shure, a lit-tle bit of Heav-en fell from out the sky one day,___ And

nes - tled on the o - cean in a spot so far a - way;___ And

when the An - gels found it, Shure it looked so sweet and fair,___ They

said sup-pose we leave it, for it looks so peace-ful there: So they

sprink-led it with star dust just to make the sham-rocks grow; ___ 'Tis the

on-ly place you'll find them no mat-ter where you go; ___ Then they dot-ted it with sil-ver, To

make it's lakes so grand, And when they had it fin-ished shure they called it Ire — land.___

Mary's A Grand Old Name

Words and Music by George M. Cohan

My moth-er's name was Ma — ry, she was so good and
Now, when her name is Ma — ry, there is no false - ness

true; _____ Be - cause her name was Ma — ry,
there; _____ When to Ma - rie she'll va - ry,

she called me Ma - ry, too._____ She was-n't gay or air - y,
she'll sure - ly bleach her hair._____ Though Ma-ry's or - di - na - ry,

but plain as she could be;_____ I hate to meet a
Ma - rie is fair to see;_____ Don't ev - er fear sweet

fair - y who calls her - self Ma - rie._____
Ma - ry, be - ware of sweet Ma - rie!

Refrain
a tempo

For it is Ma - ry, Ma - ry, plain as an - y name can

Look For The Silver Lining

Words by Bud DeSylva
Music by Jerome Kern

blue. Re-mem-ber some where the sun is shin-ing And so the right thing to do is make it shine for you. A heart, full of joy and

Ma!
(He's Making Eyes At Me)

Words by Sidney Clare
Music by Con Conrad

64

con- science guide him! Ma, _____ he wants to mar-ry me,
goin' to weak-en?

Be my hon-ey bee. _____ Ev-'ry min-ute
Ma, I'm meet-ing

he gets bold-er, Now he's lean-ing on my shoul-der, Ma, _____ He's kiss-ing
with re-sist-ance, I shall hol-ler for as-sist-ance,

1
me!" _____

2
me!" _____

McNamara's Band

Words by John J. Stamford
Music by Shamus O'Connor

Mandy

Words and Music by Irving Berlin

this.   Man - dy, _____ there's a min - is - ter

hand - y. _____   And   it   sure   would   be

dan - dy, _____   if   we'd   let   him   make   a

fee. _____   So   don't   you   lin - ger, _____

70

here's the ring for your fin - ger.

Is - n't it a hum - din - ger? Come a-long and let the

wed - ding chimes bring hap - py times, for

Man - dy and me. me.

71

Margie

Words by Benny Davis
Music by Con Conrad and
J. Russell Robinson

Moderato

You can talk a - bout your love af - fairs.____
You can pic - ture me most ev - 'ry night.____

Here's one I must tell to you;
I can't wait un - til they start.

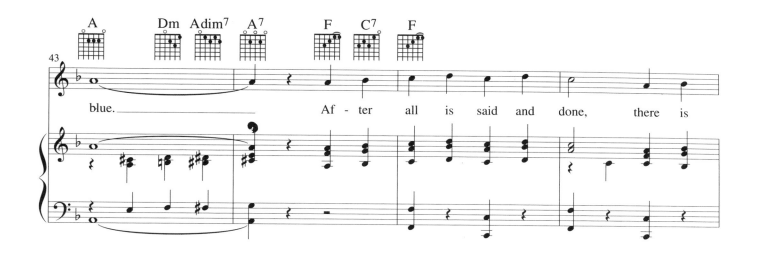

blue. _____ Af - ter all is said and done, there is

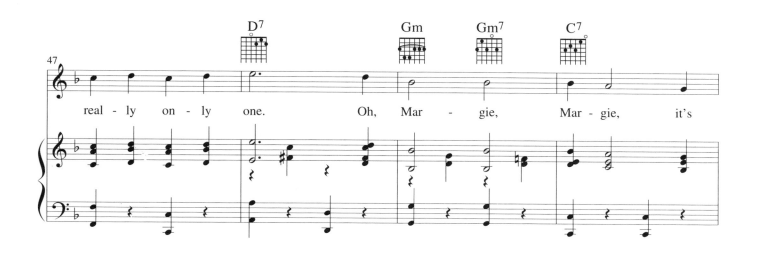

real - ly on - ly one. Oh, Mar - gie, Mar - gie, it's

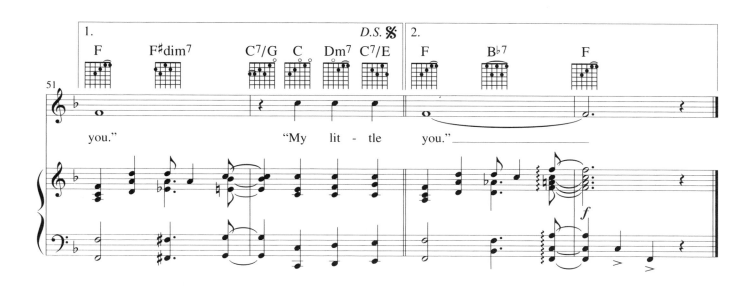

1.
you."   "My lit - tle   you." _____

2.

D.S. %

Memories

Words by Gus Kahn
Music by Egbert Van Alstyne

Child - hood days, Wild - wood days, A - mong the birds and bees,_____ You left me a - lone But still you're my own! In my beau - ti - ful MEM - O - RIES.____

Mickey

Words by Harry Williams
Music by Neil Moret

Lyrics:

Oh! what a shame they gave you the name of Mick - ey,
You had a friend that used to de - fend and love you,

Where is the rose that grows in re - pose like you?
He was a dog, a mutt of a dog, it's true;

Luck - y the birds and the bees you'd meet, Luck - y the moss and the vi - o - let sweet,
He used to fol - low you ev - 'ry - where, Look in your eyes with a lov - a - ble stare,

When they were trod by your bare lit-tle feet, There in the morn-ing dew.
He was a luck-y old dog to be there, And he be-lieved it too.

How can you blame me when I pine, Dear-ie, to change your name to mine?
This is a prom-ise true from me, "I'll be as faith-ful to you,— as he."

Refrain (Not fast)

Mick-ey, pret-ty Mick-ey, With your hair of ra-ven

hue; In your smil-ing so be-guil-ing, There's a

bit of Kil - lar - ney, bit of the Blar - ney, too.

Child - hood in the wild - wood, Like a moun - tain flow'r you

grew; Pret - ty Mick - ey, pret - ty Mick - ey, Can you

blame an - y - one for fall - ing in love with you? you?

M·I·S·S·I·S·S·I·P·P·I

Words by Bert Hanlon and Benny Ryan
Music by Harry Tierney

Moonlight Bay

Words by Edward Madden
Music by Percy Wenrich

moon beams play. _____ All a - lone _ un - known
meet once more. _____ Far a - part, _ her heart

_ they find me Mem - o - ries _ like these __ re - mind me
_ is yearn - ing, With a sigh _ for my __ re - turn - ing,

Of the girl _ I left __ be - hind me, Down on Moon - light Bay.
With the light _ of love __ still burn - ing, As in days of yore.

CHORUS

We were sail - ing a long _____ On Moon - light

p-f

Bay, _____ We could hear the voic-es ring - ing, _____ They seemed to

say _____ "You have stol - en my heart, _____

_ Now don't go 'way!" _____ As we sang Love's Old Sweet

Song, On Moon - light Bay. _____ We were sail - ing a - _

84

M·O·T·H·E·R
(A Word That Means The World To Me)

Words by Howard Johnson
Music by Theodore Morse

"T" is for the tears were shed to save me,

"H" is for her heart of pur-est gold,

"E" is for her eyes, with love-light shin - ing,

My Buddy

Words by Gus Kahn
Music by Walter Donaldson

Pretty Baby

Words by Gus Kahn
Music by Tony Jackson and Egbert Van Alstyne

My Mammy

Words by Sam M. Lewis and Joe Young
Music by Walter Donaldson

Moderately (with a light beat)

93

Oh, Johnny, Oh!

Words by Ed Rose
Music by Abe Olman

Pack Up Your Troubles In Your Old Kit Bag
(And Smile, Smile, Smile)

Words by George Asaf
Music by Felix Powell

Peg O' My Heart

Words by Alfred Bryan
Music by Fred Fisher

Oh! my heart's in a whirl, __ o - ver one lit - tle girl, __ I love her, I love __ her, yes, I

When your heart's full of fears, __ and your eyes full of tears, __ I'll kiss them, I'll kiss __ them all a -

A Pretty Girl Is Like A Melody

Words and Music by Irving Berlin

Rock-A-Bye Your Baby With A Dixie Melody

Words by Sam M. Lewis and Joe Young
Music by Jean Schwartz

Rose Of Washington Square

Words by Ballard MacDonald
Music by James F. Hanley

child of the ci - ty grows ___ A but - ter - fly flew to the gar - den ___ From
cheek of the blush-ing rose ___ The gay but - ter - fly's wings are fold - ed ___ The
he - mi - an Hon - ky Tonks ___ One day I met Har - ri - son Fish - er ___ Said
Ve - nus ain't got no arms ___ Rube Gold-berg my fi - gure ad - mi - res ___ He

out of the blue sky a - bove ___ The heart of the rose set a -
heart of the rose has grown cold ___ A but - ter - fly lives but a
he "You're like ro - ses, the stems ___ I want you to pose for a
dress - es me up in a veil ___ And u - ses my shape for the

flut - ter ___ With a won - der - ful tale of love ___ He
sea - son ___ And a rose in a week grows old ___ The
pic - ture ___ On the cov - er of "Jim Jam Jems" ___ *And*
pic - tures ___ That he draws in the Ev - 'ning Mail ___ He

told her of birds and of bees ___ Of the brooks and the meadows and trees He whisper'd:
mea-dows, the brooks and the trees ___ Like the birds and the flowers and bees Need sunshine:
that's how I first got my start ___ Now my life is de - vo - ted to art They call me:
prom - ised sometime when he's free ___ That he'll mod - el a sta - tue of me They call me:

rit.

Jim Jam Jems a famous satirical magazine of yesteryear.

The Sheik Of Araby

Words by Harry B. Smith and Francis Wheeler
Music by Ted Snyder

O- ver the des - ert wild and free
While stars are fad - ing in the dawn _____

Rides the bold Shiek of Ar - a - by. _____
O - ver the des - ert they'll be gone; _____

His A - rab band At his com - mand,
His cap - tured bride Close by his side;

Fol - low his love's car - a - van. _____
Swift as the wind they will ride. _____

Un - der the shad - ow of the palms; _____
Proud - ly he scorns her smile or tear; _____

He sings to call her to his arms. _____
Soon he will con - quer love by fear. _____

Smiles

Words and Music by
J. Will Callahan and Lee S. Roberts

There are smiles _____ that make us hap - py, _____ there are

smiles _____ that make us blue; _____ There are smiles that

steal a - way the tear - drops ___ as the sun - beams steal a - way the

Somebody Stole My Gal

Words and Music by Leo Wood

Swanee

Words by Irving Caesar
Music by George Gershwin

Till We Meet Again

Words by Raymond B. Egan
Music by Richard A. Whiting

CHORUS *a tempo*

Smile the while you kiss me sad a-dieu When the clouds roll by I'll come to you Then the skies will seem more blue Down in lov-ers lane my dear-ie Wed-ding bells will ring so mer-ri-ly Ev'-ry tear will be a mem-o-ry So wait and pray each night for me Till we meet a-gain -gain

Toot, Toot, Tootsie, Goodbye

Words and Music by Gus Kahn,
Ernie Erdman, Dan Russo and Ted Fiorito

133

Three O'Clock In The Morning

Words by **Dorothy Terriss**
Music by **Julian Robledo**

'Way Down Yonder In New Orleans

By Henry Creamer and J. Turner Layton

give your la-dy fair _____ a lit-tle smile" Stop! You bet your

life you'll lin-ger there _____ a lit-tle while

There is Heav-en right

They've got an - gels right

here on earth _____ With those beau - ti - ful queens

here on earth _____ Wear - ing lit - tle blue jeans

'Way Down Yon - der In

New Or - leans. leans. _____

When The Saints Go Marching In

Traditional

Brightly

PIANO

mf

CHORUS *with spirit*

Tacet

F

1. Oh, when the saints _____ go march - ing
2. (Oh, when the) sun _____ re - fuse to
3. (Oh, when they) crown _____ Him Lord of
4. (Oh, when they) gath - - - er 'round the

mf

in, _____ Oh, when the saints go march - ing
shine, _____ Oh, when the sun re - fuse to
All, _____ Oh, when the crown Him Lord of
throne, _____ Oh, when the gath - er 'round the

Whispering

**Words and Music by John Schonberger,
Richard Coburn and Vincent Rose**

Take This Magazine To Your Piano!

(It's Filled With Wonderful Music To Play)

PianoToday

FORMERLY KEYBOARD CLASSICS & PIANO STYLIST

Alfred Brendel
uncovering music's DNA

The Classical
Roland Hanna

Terry Riley
New Music from
Minimalism's Godfather

Taking It All In Stride
*Mike Lipskin &
Judy Carmichael*

Each issue is filled with the greatest classical and romantic themes of all time... and the most stylish pop and jazz arrangements of today. You'll love our music, and treasure our self-improvement features. Top piano professionals in every area of music — from Van Cliburn and André Watts to Dave Brubeck and George Shearing — use our pages to share their how-to's, tips and trade secrets with you!

Complete Piano Scores!

When you subscribe to *Piano Today*, you get the soaring melodies of the Romantic Era... the fire of Beethoven... and the jazziness of Gershwin. Plus the most sophisticated, elegant and swinging arrangements of pop hits from the likes of Dick Hyman, George Shearing, and Oscar Peterson. You receive over a dozen great pieces of music in each and every issue, for less than 40¢ each. (Sheet music in stores today costs nearly 10 times as much!) Plus plenty of surprises, too, like premieres by George Gershwin, Stephen Foster, Harold Arlen, J.S. Bach, Chick Corea and others!

Special Section For Beginners!

If you are just starting, or a bit rusty, you'll enjoy the bonus section for early level pianists, with easy pieces and arrangements that anyone can play. There are "Finger Fitness" and theory lessons geared to the needs of pianists who have been playing just a short time, or who are returning to the piano after many years away from it. Playing and learning has never been easier... or more enjoyable!

Here's A Free Gift... A $9.95 Value!

You can get a free copy of our music book *Great Piano Themes*. You'll love these beautiful piano pieces gathered from the best of both the classical and jazz traditions. Enjoy full piano arrangements of **Canon** Pachelbel • **Tango** Albeniz • **Clair de Lune** Debussy • **Solace** Joplin • **To A Wild Rose** MacDowell • **Oriental** Manzanares • **Elegie** Massenet • **Odeon** Nazareth • **Theme From Piano Concerto No. 2** Rachmaninoff • **Yamekraw** Johnson • **Jelly Roll Blues** Morton • **Traümerei** Schumann • **Nervous Blues** Bradford • **Gymnopedie No. 1** Satie.

We want you to play and enjoy these wonderful pieces as our gift, just for trying PIANO TODAY, a quarterly music magazine!

Piano Today PO Box 58837, Boulder, CO 80322-8837

YES, send my FREE copy of *Great Piano Themes* and enter my subscription to Piano Today as checked below. I understand that I may cancel at anytime and receive a refund on all unmailed issues. The free copy of *Great Piano Themes* is mine to keep in any case.

(✓) check one

☐ One Year $18.97   ☐ Two Years $35.00

☐ I enclose full payment of $_____ (Make check payable to Piano Today)

Charge to my: ☐ MasterCard   ☐ Visa

Signature_____

Account No. _____ Exp. Date _____

Name_____

Address_____

City _____ State_____ Zip _____

Canadian residents please add $5.00 per year extra for postage.   5SAZ1

150 Songs With Just 3 Chords

★ **Perfect For Beginners!**

★ **Learn Chord Progressions Easily!**

★ **Memorize Songs Instantly!**

Believe it or not … dozens and dozens of pop tunes can be played using just 3 chords! Here is a collection of 150 of them … from "Auld Lang Syne" and "Camptown Races" to "Bill Bailey," "Jingle Bells," "Little Brown Jug," "When The Saints Go Marchin' In," "Merry Widow Waltz," and much, much more!

This book is perfect for beginners, or anyone who would like to study the basics of chord progressions. For keyboardists who thought it would take years to memorize these songs, it will be a revelation. Imagine … 150 well-known tunes that use no more than 3 chords! Be prepared for your next singalong; and don't bother to bring any music with you!

Your Guarantee

We are sure you will be thrilled and delighted with these great songs using just three chords. If you are unhappy with this book for any reason whatsoever, just return it within 30 days for a full refund. No questions asked! You have absolutely nothing to lose, so order your copy TODAY!

HERE ARE JUST A FEW OF THE 150 SONGS USING 3 CHORDS!

Hello Ma Baby • Amazing Grace • Down By The Riverside • St. James Infirmary • Swing Low, Sweet Chariot • Merry Widow Waltz • America • Auld Lang Syne • Dark Eyes • Bill Bailey • Deck The Halls • I Love You Truly • Jingle Bells • My Darling Clementine • Put Your Arms Around Me Honey • Rock Of Ages • Silent Night • Sidewalks Of New York • When You And I Were Young, Maggie • When the Saints Go Marchin' In • Silver Threads Among The Gold • Sweet Molly Malone • Little Brown Jug • Santa Lucia • Come Josephine In My Flying Machine • much, much more!

★ ★ ★ HOW TO ORDER ★ ★ ★

Write down the number of copies of **150 Songs With Just 3 Chords** you want. For each volume ordered, enclose check or money order for $16.95 plus $3.50 postage and handling payable to Songbooks Unlimited (NJ, IA and NY residents please add sales tax), payable to Songbooks Unlimited. Mail to: SONGBOOKS UNLIMITED, P.O. Box 1950, Ridgely M.D. 21681-1950. Specify product #900654. We will ship promptly with full 30-day money-back guarantee.

For Fastest Credit Card Service Call Toll Free
1-800-641-9797
24 Hours A Day, 7 Days A Week!